THE FABER BOOK OF

CLASSICAL

FILM THEMES

arranged for easy piano/keyboard

by Daniel Scott

FABER MUSIC

CONTENTS

These arrangements © 1988 by Faber Music Ltd
First published in 1988 by Faber Music Ltd
3 Queen Square, London WC1N 3AU
Music drawn by Christopher Hinkins
Cover illustration and typography by John Bury
Printed in England by Halstan & Co Ltd

1. 2001

(J. Strauss: The Blue Danube Waltz)

STRINGS

Waltz tempo

2. A Clockwork Orange

(L. van Beethoven: *Ode to Joy* from Symphony No. 9)

TRUMPET/FLUTE

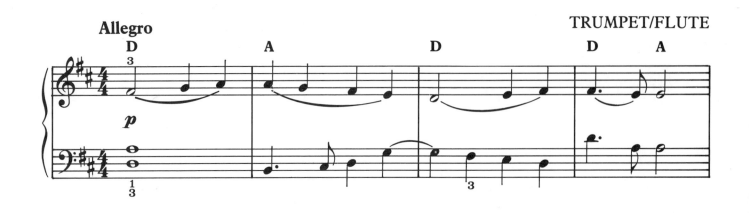

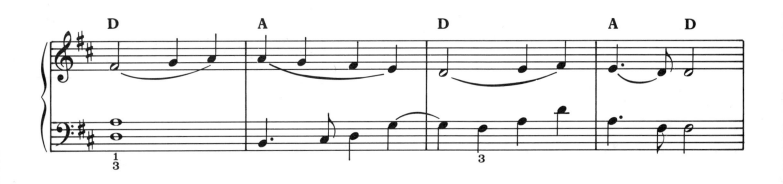

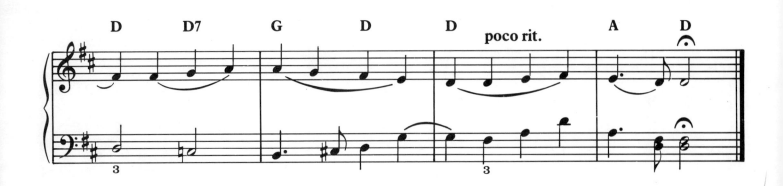

3. Elvira Madigan

(W.A. Mozart: Piano Concerto in C, K.467, slow movement)

PIANO

4. Barry Lyndon (i)

(F. Schubert: Piano Trio No. 2, slow movement)

VIOLIN/PIANO

5. Manhattan

(G. Gershwin: Rhapsody in Blue)

CLARINET/PIANO

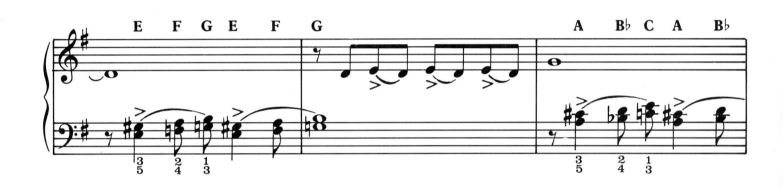

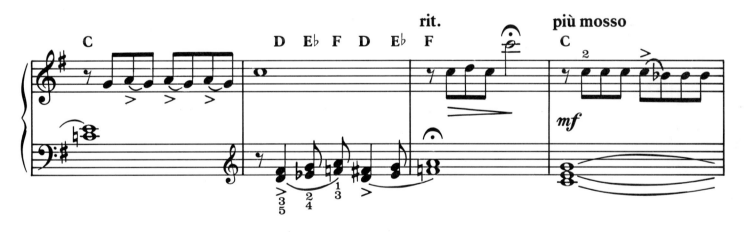

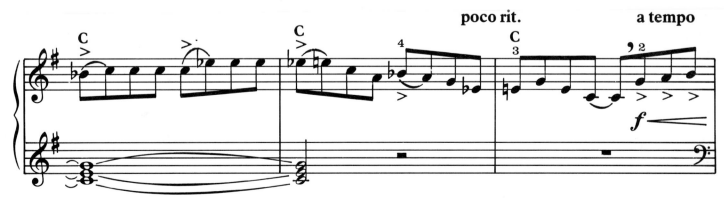

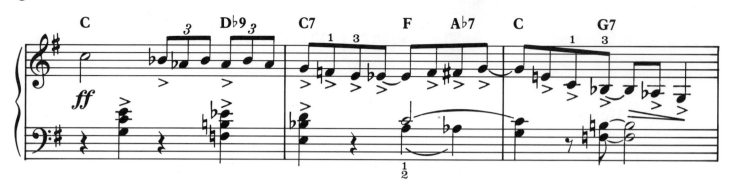

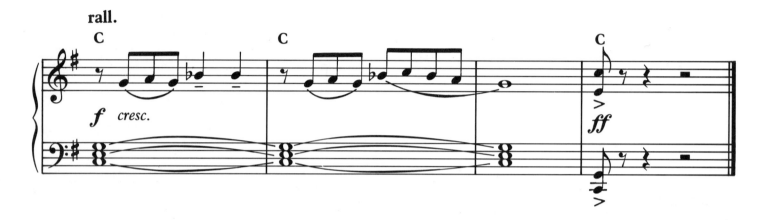

6. Waterloo Bridge

(P. Tchaikovsky: Theme from *Swan Lake*)

OBOE/HARP

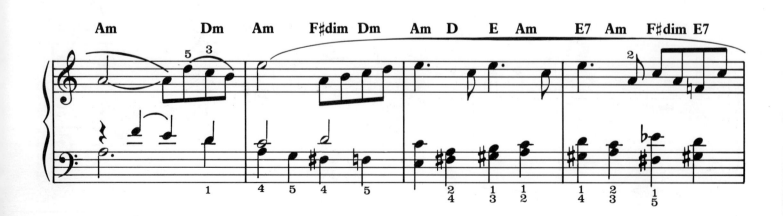

7. Barry Lyndon (ii)

(G.F. Handel: Sarabande from Suite No. XI)

FLUTE/VIOLIN

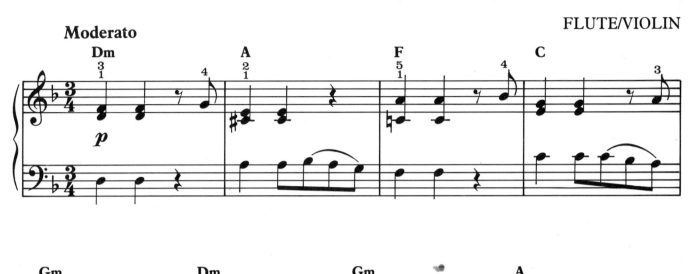

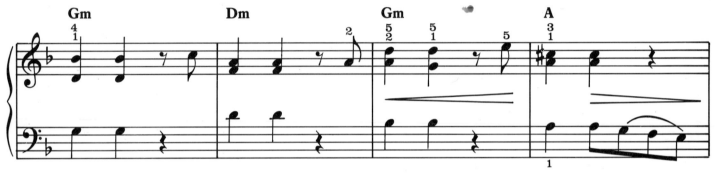

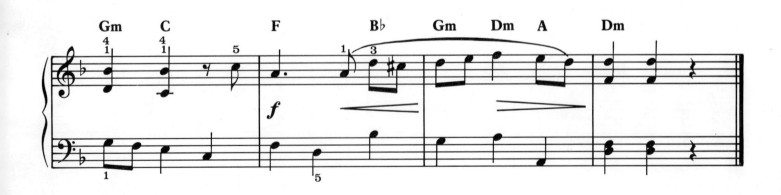

8. The Music Lovers

(P. Tchaikovsky: Theme from Piano Concerto No. 1)

PIANO

9. Out of Africa

(W.A. Mozart: Clarinet Concerto, K.622, slow movement)

CLARINET/PIANO/ELEC. PIANO

*Upper D first time, lower D second time.

10. A Room with a View

(G. Puccini: *O mio babbino caro* from *Gianni Schicchi*)

11. Death in Venice

(G. Mahler: Adagietto from Symphony No. 5)

STRINGS

12. A Midsummer Night's Sex Comedy

(F. Mendelssohn: Wedding March from *A Midsummer Night's Dream*)

ORGAN

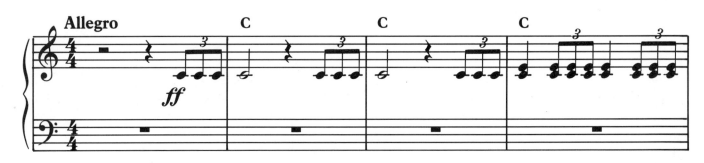

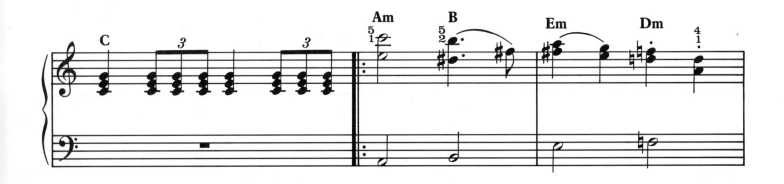

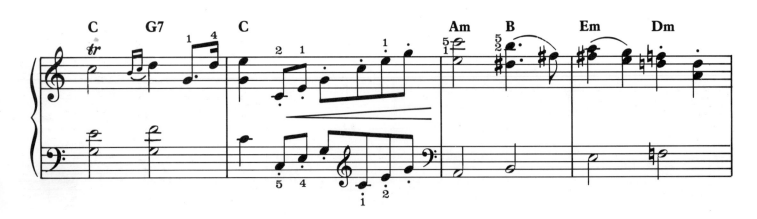

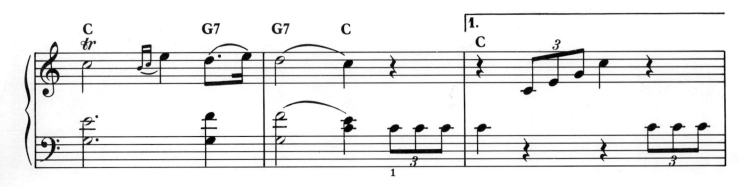

13. Kismet

(A. Borodin: Polovtsian Dance from *Prince Igor*)

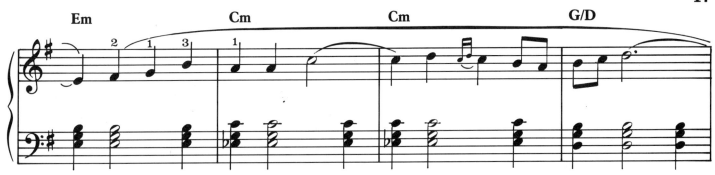

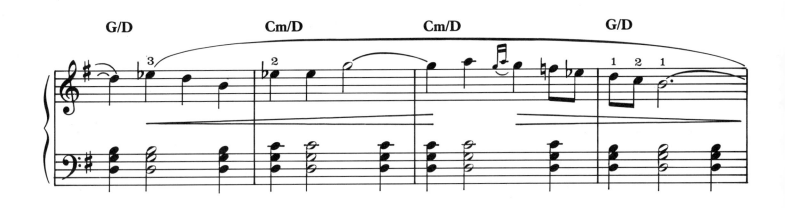

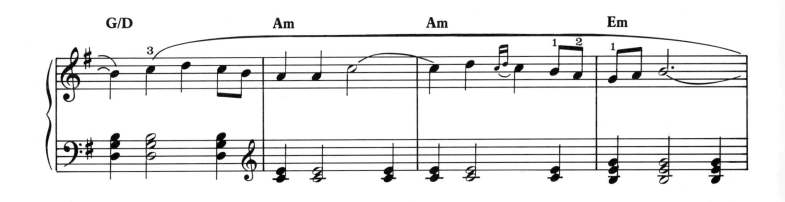

18

14. Apocalypse Now

(R. Wagner: The Ride of the Valkyries)

BRASS

15. Gallipoli

(T. Albinoni: Adagio)

ORGAN/STRINGS

16. 10

(M. Ravel: Bolero)

SAXOPHONE/SYNTH

Tempo di bolero (♩=72)

17. Song of Norway

(E. Grieg: Theme from Piano Concerto)

PIANO

18. Diva

(A. Catalani: *Ne andrò lontana* from *La Wally*)

19. Brief Encounter

(S. Rachmaninov: Theme from Piano Concerto No. 2, slow movement)

PIANO

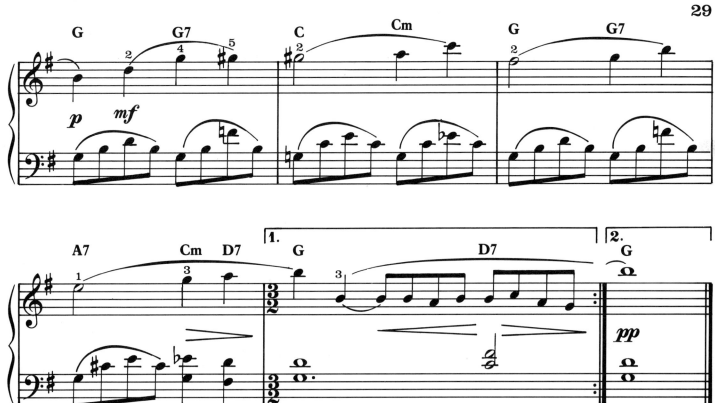

20. The Ladykillers

(L. Boccherini: Minuet)

FLUTE

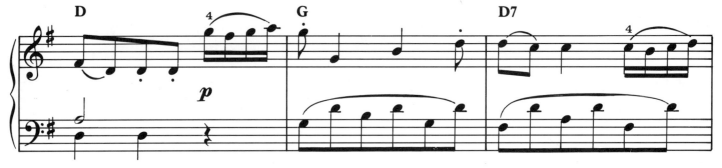

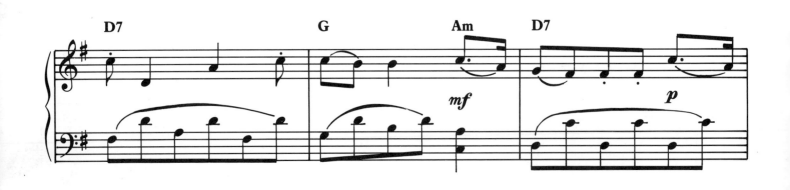

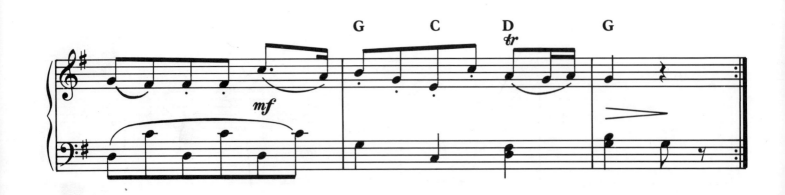